Creative

ARITHMETIC BOOK FOR CHILDREN

NUMBER-BOOK

FOR
PLAY GROUP

CONCEPT AND ILLUSTRATION

GANESHAN

M.Fine/Ph.D.(Applied Art)

PILGRIMS PUBLISHING
◆ Varanasi ◆

www.pilgrimsbooks.com

Creative Arithmetic Book for Children—Number-Book
Ganeshan

Published by:
PILGRIMS PUBLISHING

An imprint of:
PILGRIMS BOOK HOUSE
(Distributors in India)
B 27/98 A-8, Nawabganj Road
Durga Kund, Varanasi-221010, India
Tel: 91-542- 2314060, Fax: 91-542- 2312456
E-mail: pilgrims@satyam.net.in
Website: www.pilgrimsbooks.com

First Edition
Copyright © 2007, Ganeshan
All Rights Reserved

ISBN: 81-7769-468-5

Printed in India at Pilgrim Press Pvt. Ltd. Lalpur Varanasi

WRITE 1

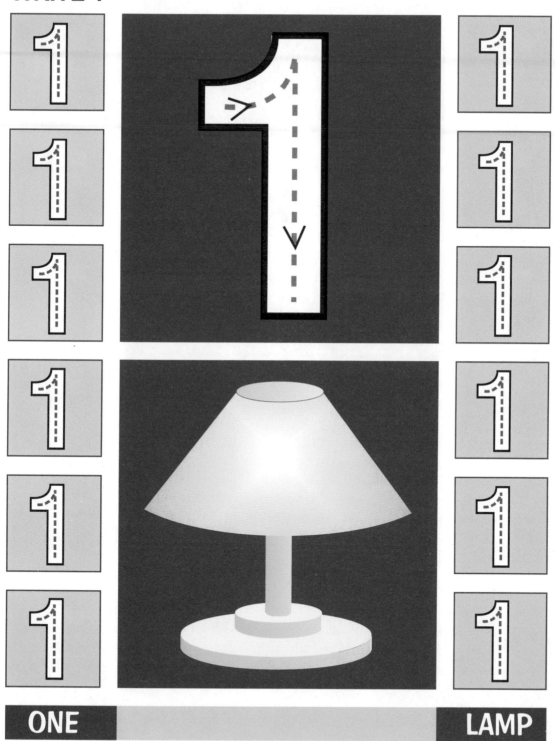

ONE LAMP

WRITE 1

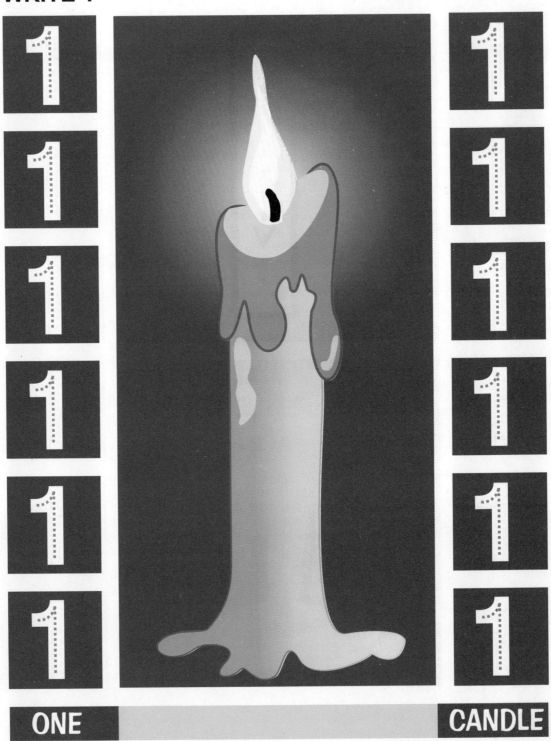

ONE   CANDLE

NOW, COUNT AND WRITE

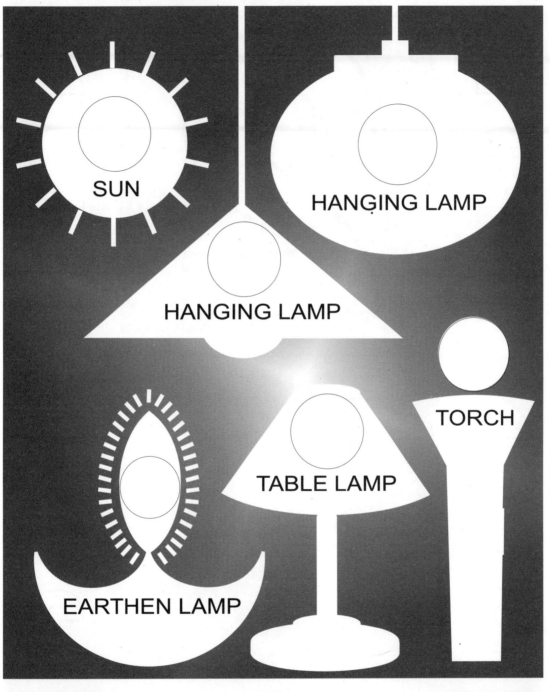

SUN

HANGING LAMP

HANGING LAMP

TORCH

TABLE LAMP

EARTHEN LAMP

ONE | ONE

WRITE 2

TWO **FISHES**

WRITE 2

TWO

OCTOPUSES

TWO

FROGS

TWO

TURTLES

NOW, COUNT AND WRITE

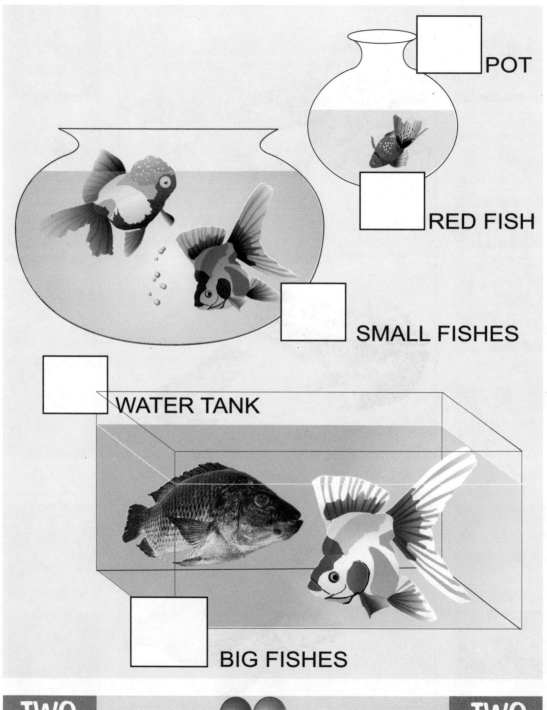

POT

RED FISH

SMALL FISHES

WATER TANK

BIG FISHES

WRITE 3

THREE

ANIMALS

WRITE 3

CATS

DOGS

COWS

THREE   THREE

NOW, COUNT AND WRITE

THREE  THREE

FOUR **BIRDS**

NOW, COUNT AND WRITE

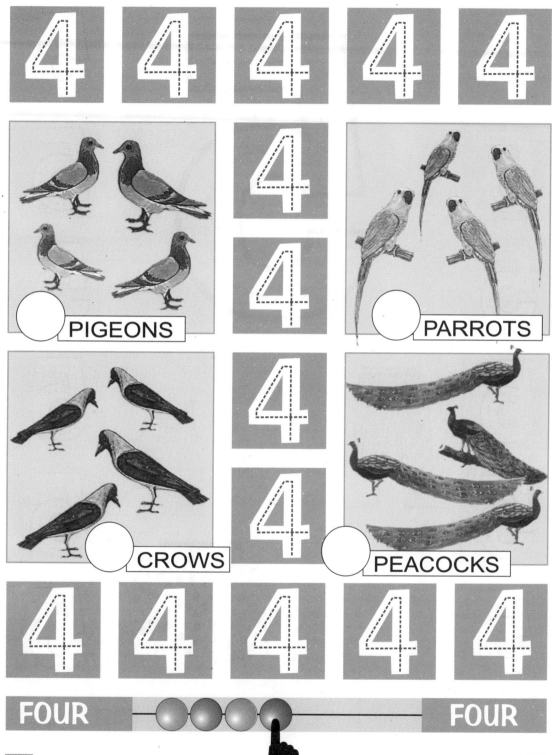

PIGEONS

PARROTS

CROWS

PEACOCKS

FOUR

FOUR

WRITE 5

1 2 3 4 5

FIVE   DRESSES

COUNT AND WRITE

VESTS

TROUSERS

FROCKS

SKIRTS

SHIRTS

FIVE   FIVE

NOW, COUNT AND WRITE HOW MANY DRESSES?

DRESSES

SKIRTS

TROUSERS

DRESSES

VESTS

FROCK

DRESSES

SHIRTS

FROCKS

SAY AND WRITE 6

SIX

UTENSILS

17

COUNT AND WRITE

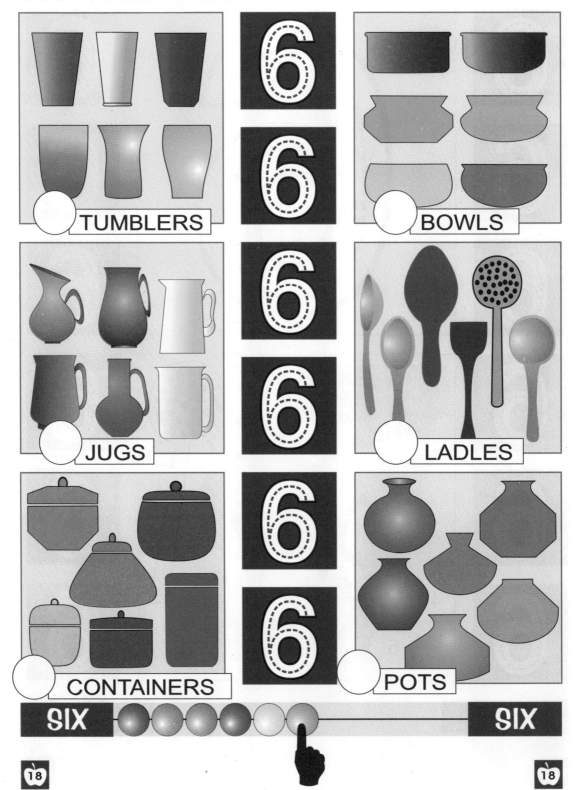

6

6

TUMBLERS

BOWLS

6

6

JUGS

LADLES

6

6

CONTAINERS

POTS

SIX

SIX

DRAW THE UTENSILS AND WRITE THE NUMBERS

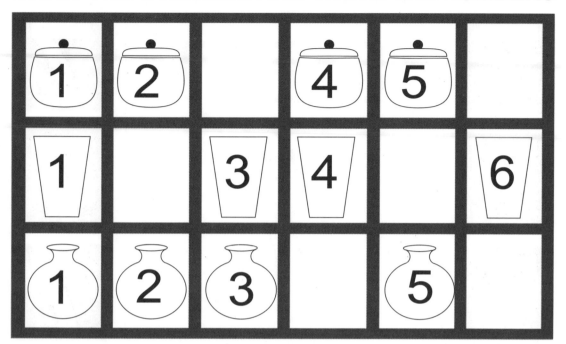

WRITE THE MISSING NUMBERS

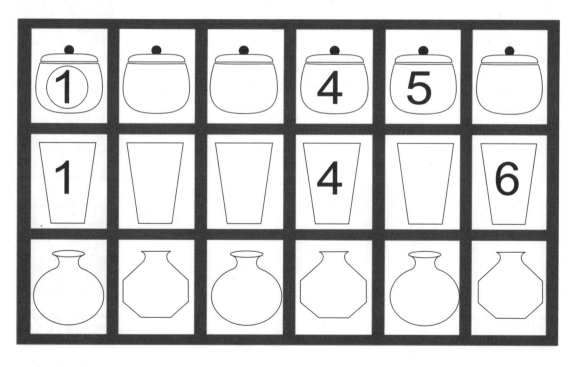

COUNT AND WRITE 7

SEVEN

FRUITS

HOW MANY FRUITS ?

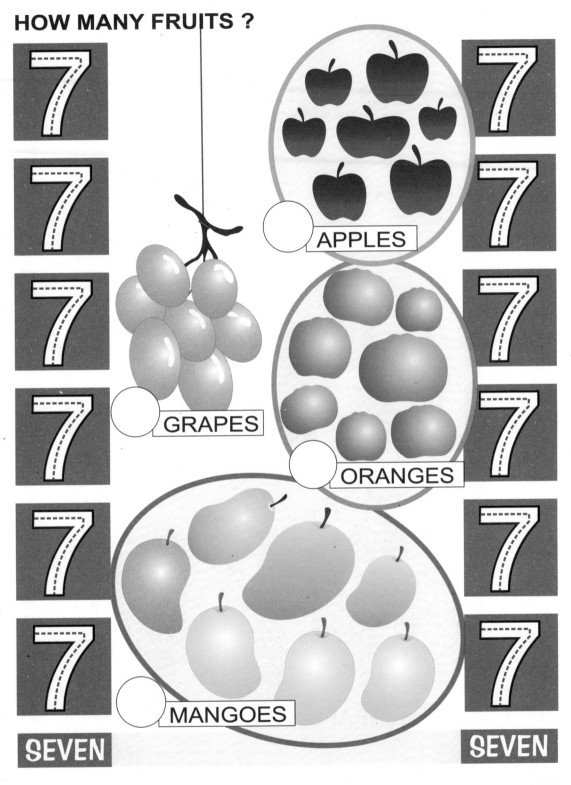

APPLES

GRAPES

ORANGES

MANGOES

SEVEN   SEVEN

21   21

HOW MANY FRUITS ?

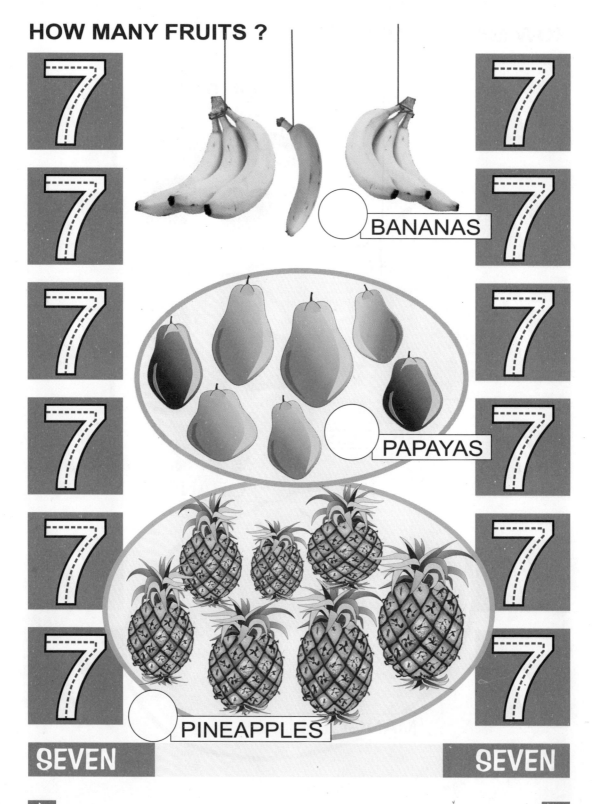

BANANAS

PAPAYAS

PINEAPPLES

SEVEN

SEVEN

HOW MANY FRUITS ?

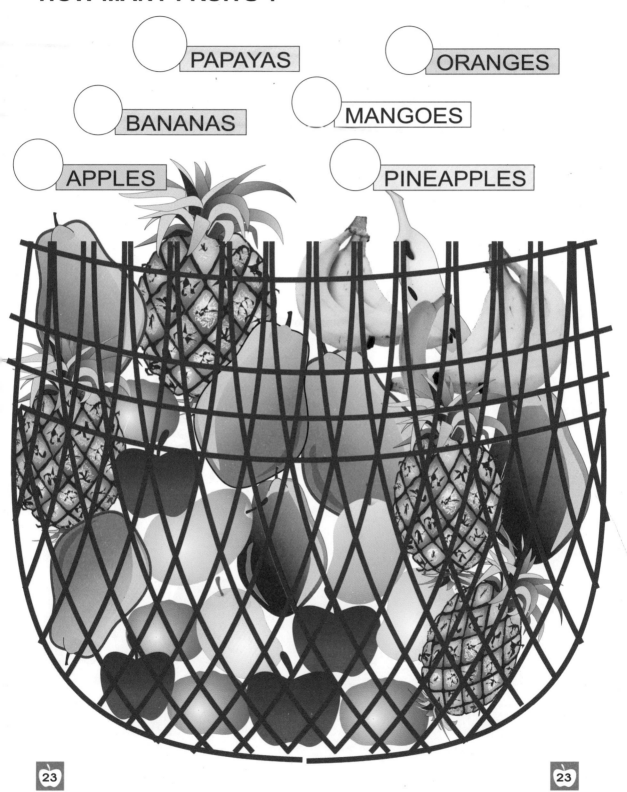

PAPAYAS

ORANGES

BANANAS

MANGOES

APPLES

PINEAPPLES

23

WRITE 8

1 2 3 4 5 6 7 8

EIGHT

FLOWERS

NOW,COUNT AND WRITE

1.Marigold

2.Lotus

3.Water Lily

4.Sunflower

5.Dahlia

6.Rose

7.Champa

8.Flax

EIGHT **FLOWERS**

COUNT AND WRITE

LOTUSES

WRITE 9

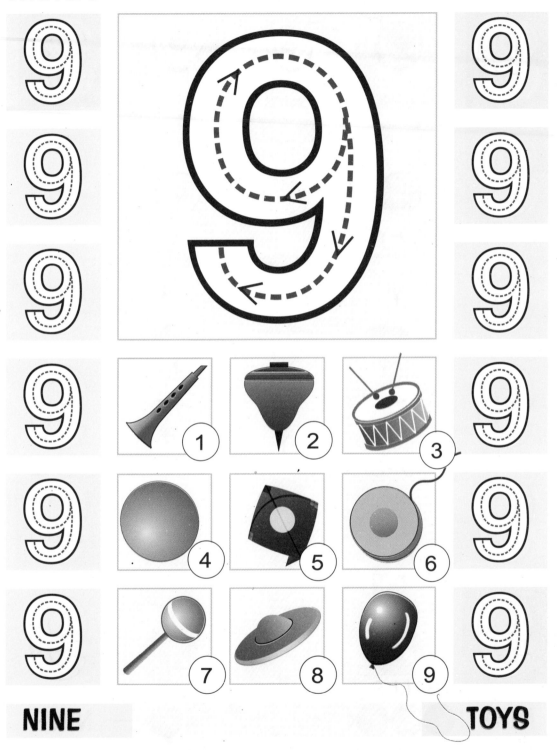

NINE

TOYS

NOW, COUNT AND WRITE

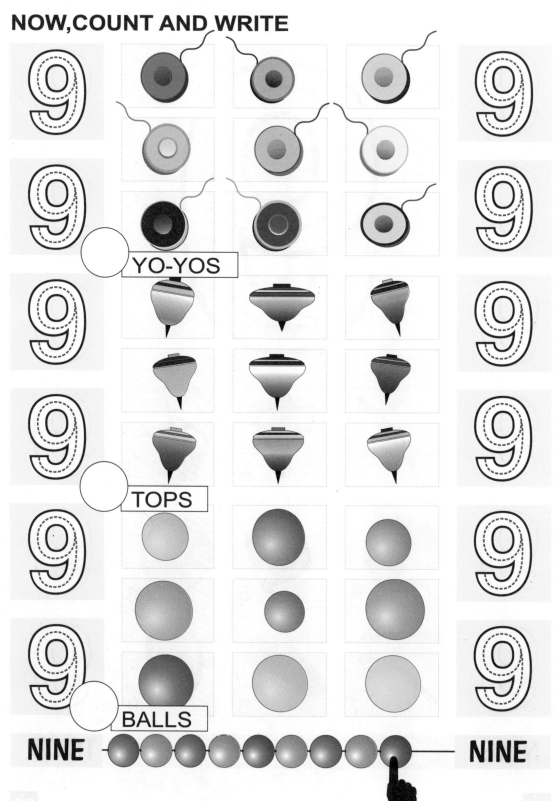

YO-YOS

TOPS

BALLS

NINE — NINE

WRITE 9

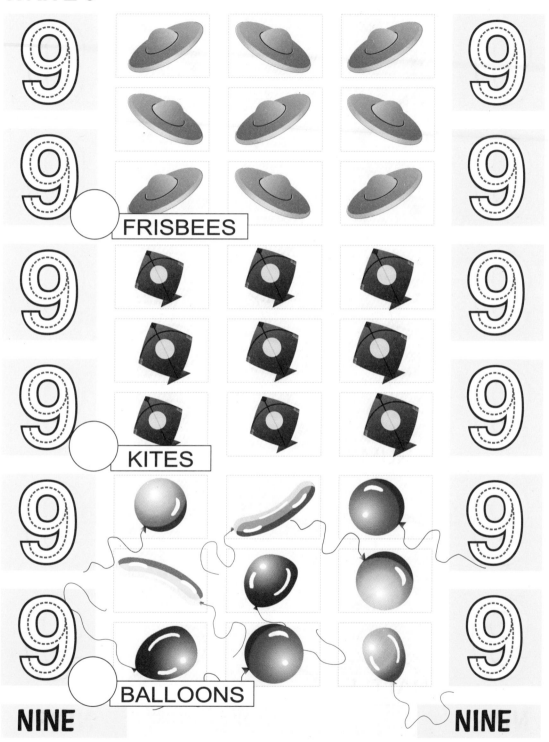

FRISBEES

KITES

BALLOONS

NINE

NINE

WRITE 9

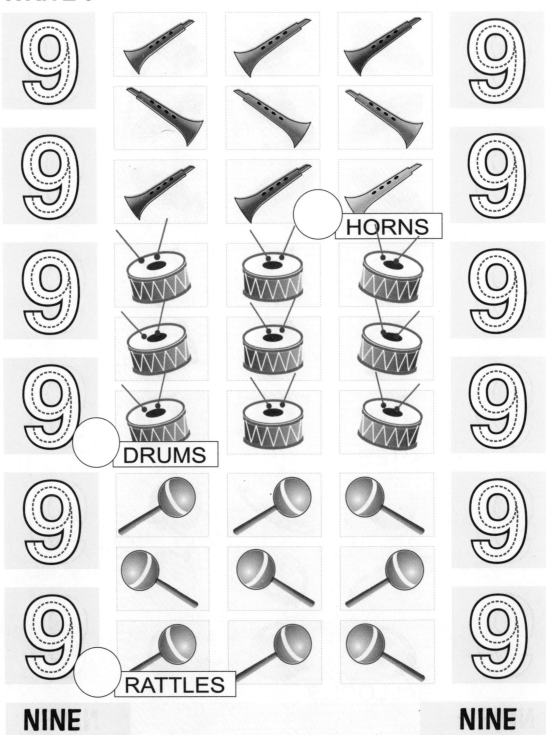

HORNS

DRUMS

RATTLES

NINE

NINE

WRITE 10

TEN   **THINGS**

NOW, COUNT AND WRITE

10 10

10 10

10 10

SPOONS

10 10

10 10

10 10

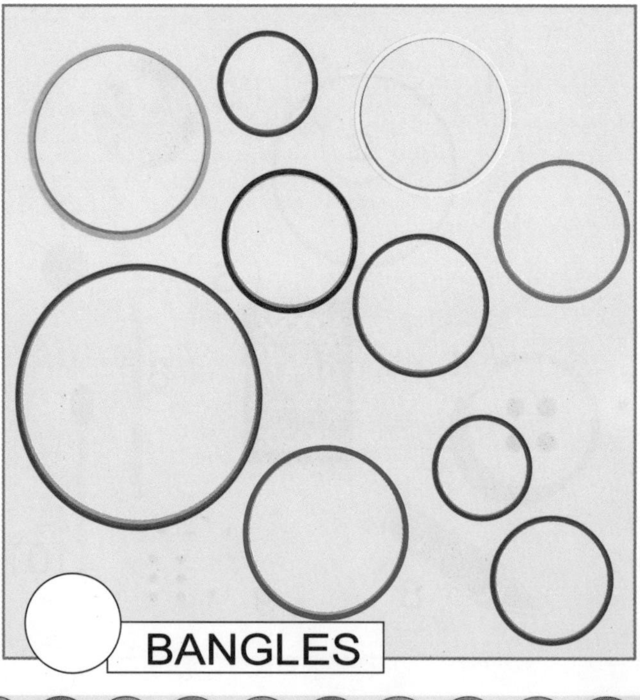

BANGLES

TEN 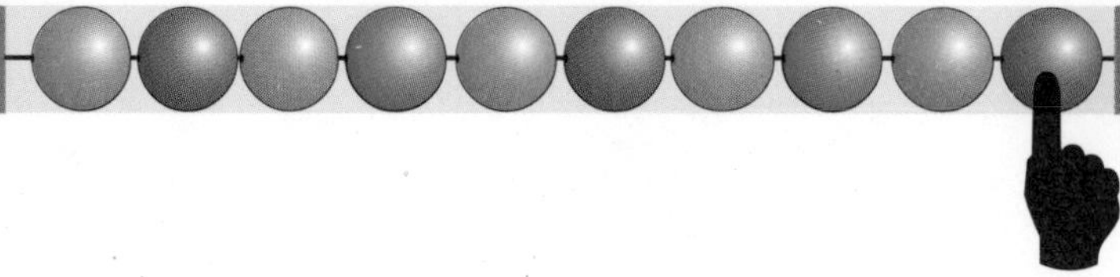 TEN

WRITE 10

10 10 10 10 10 10 10 10

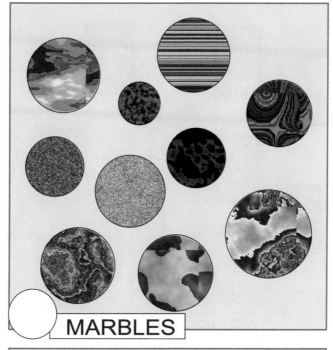

MARBLES

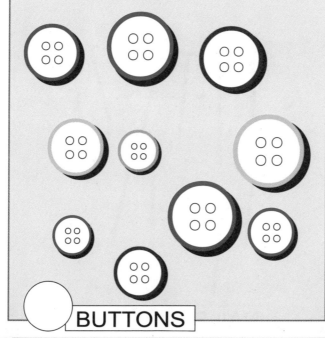

BUTTONS

TEN

TEN

33 33

WRITE 10

10 10

10 10

10 10

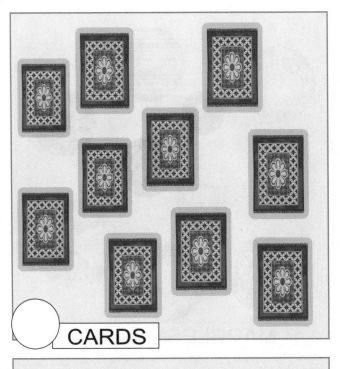

CARDS

10 10

10 10

10 10

NAILS

TEN TEN

34 34

WRITE 10

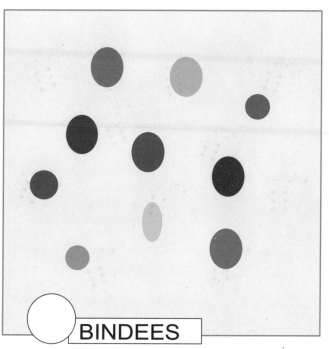

BINDEES

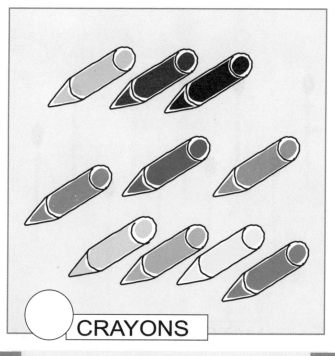

CRAYONS

TEN

TEN

WRITE 10

10 **10**

10 **10**

10 **10**

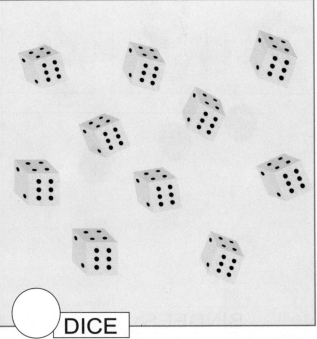

DICE

10 **10**

10 **10**

10 **10**

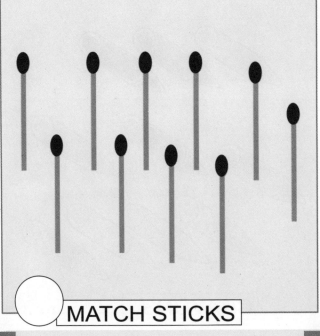

MATCH STICKS

TEN TEN

WRITE 1 TO 5

1	2	3	4	5

WRITE 1 TO 5

WRITE 6 TO 10

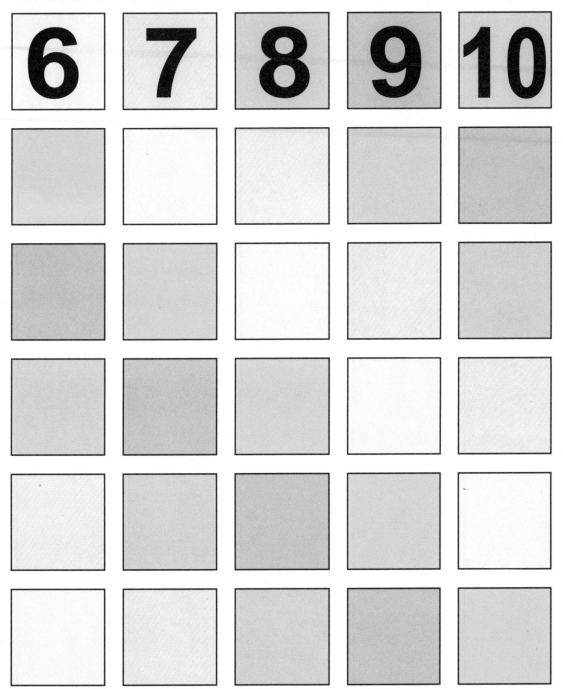

WRITE 6 TO 10